Ladybird Readers

Washing Day

Series Editor: Sorrel Pitts
Text adapted by Hazel Geatches
Activities written by Kamini Khanduri

LADYBIRD BOOKS

UK | USA | Canada | Ireland | Australia
India | New Zealand | South Africa

Ladybird Books is part of the Penguin Random House group of companies
whose addresses can be found at global.penguinrandomhouse.com.
www.penguin.co.uk www.puffin.co.uk www.ladybird.co.uk

First published 2020
001

Masha and the Bear series created by: O. Kuzovkov
Masha and the Bear Art Director: I. Trusov

Printed in China

A CIP catalogue record for this book is available from the British Library

ISBN: 978-0-241-40181-1

All correspondence to:
Ladybird Books
Penguin Random House Children's
80 Strand, London WC2R 0RL

Washing Day

Based on the
Masha and the Bear TV series

Picture words

Masha

Bear

Pig Rosie

Bear's house

Masha's house

washing

shower

wash

wet

jam

tired

Pig Rosie is listening to music.

"Let's play!" says Masha.
"I'm your mommy.
You're my baby."

"I want some milk for my baby," says Masha.

"Bear has milk!"
says Masha.

“Let’s go to Bear’s house!” says Masha.

Bear is doing his washing.

Here comes Pig Rosie!
Here comes Masha!

Oh no! Masha is dirty!

“Can I have some milk for my baby, please?” says Masha.

Masha has a shower.

Bear washes Masha's clothes.

Now, the clothes are clean and wet. Masha is clean and wet, too!

Bear makes new clothes.

"Oh, I like my new clothes!" says Masha.

Masha goes to the kitchen.
She finds some milk.

Oh no! Masha is dirty again!

Masha has a shower.

Bear washes Masha's clothes. Then, he makes new clothes.

Masha goes to the kitchen.
She finds some food.

"Oh, nice!" says Masha.

Masha eats the food.
Oh no! She is dirty again.

Masha has a shower.
Bear makes new clothes.

Masha finds some jam.
She is dirty again!

Bear is tired. He cannot
make new clothes.

Now, Masha is clean, but her clothes are wet!

Bear gives Masha the baby clothes.

Now, Masha is the baby, and
Pig Rosie is the mommy.

Pig Rosie is happy!
Bear is happy, too!

Activities

The key below describes the skills practiced in each activity.

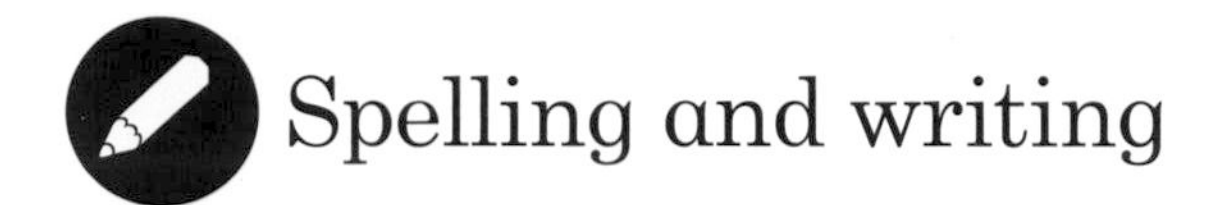
Spelling and writing

Reading

Speaking

Critical thinking

Preparation for the Cambridge Young Learners exams

1 Match the words to the pictures. 

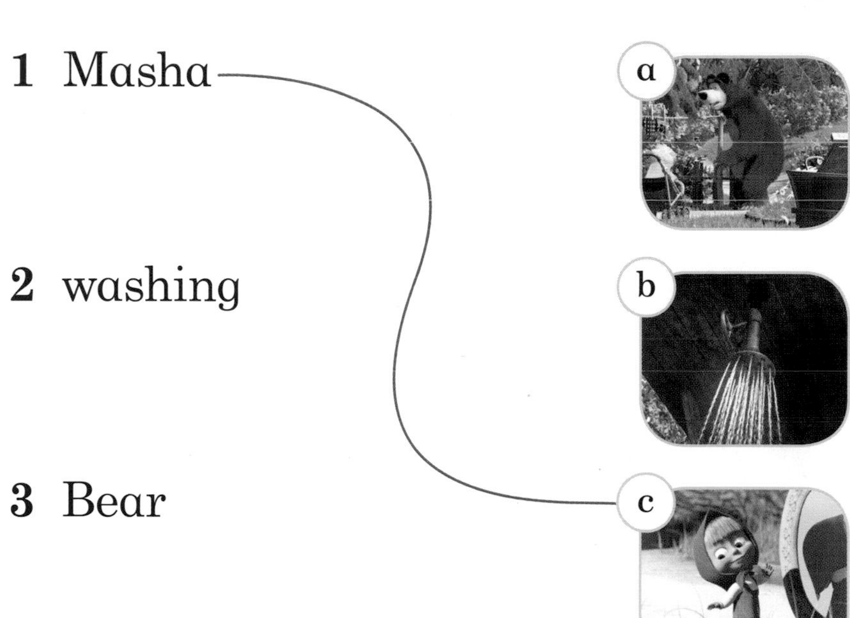

1 Masha

2 washing

3 Bear

4 jam

5 Pig Rosie

6 shower

a b c d e f

2 Circle the correct words. 

1 Pig Rosie is listening to

a music.

b Masha.

2 Masha says,

a "Let's eat!"

b "Let's play!"

3 She says,

a "I'm your baby."

b "I'm your mommy."

3 Circle the correct words. 

1 Pig Rosie is the **mommy. / baby.**

2 Masha **wants / drinks** some milk.

3 Masha wants **juice / milk** for her baby.

4 **"Bear / "Pig Rosie** has milk!" says Masha.

4 Ask and answer the questions with a friend.

1 Where does Masha go?

She goes to Bear's house.

2 What is Pig Rosie wearing?

She is wearing . . .

3 Do they drive to Bear's house?

No, they . . .

5 Look and read. Choose the correct words and write them on the lines.

comes dirty Masha milk

1 Here ......comes...... Pig Rosie!

2 Here comes ....!

3 Oh no! Masha is ....!

4 "Can I have some ....
for my baby, please?" says Masha.

6 Match the words.

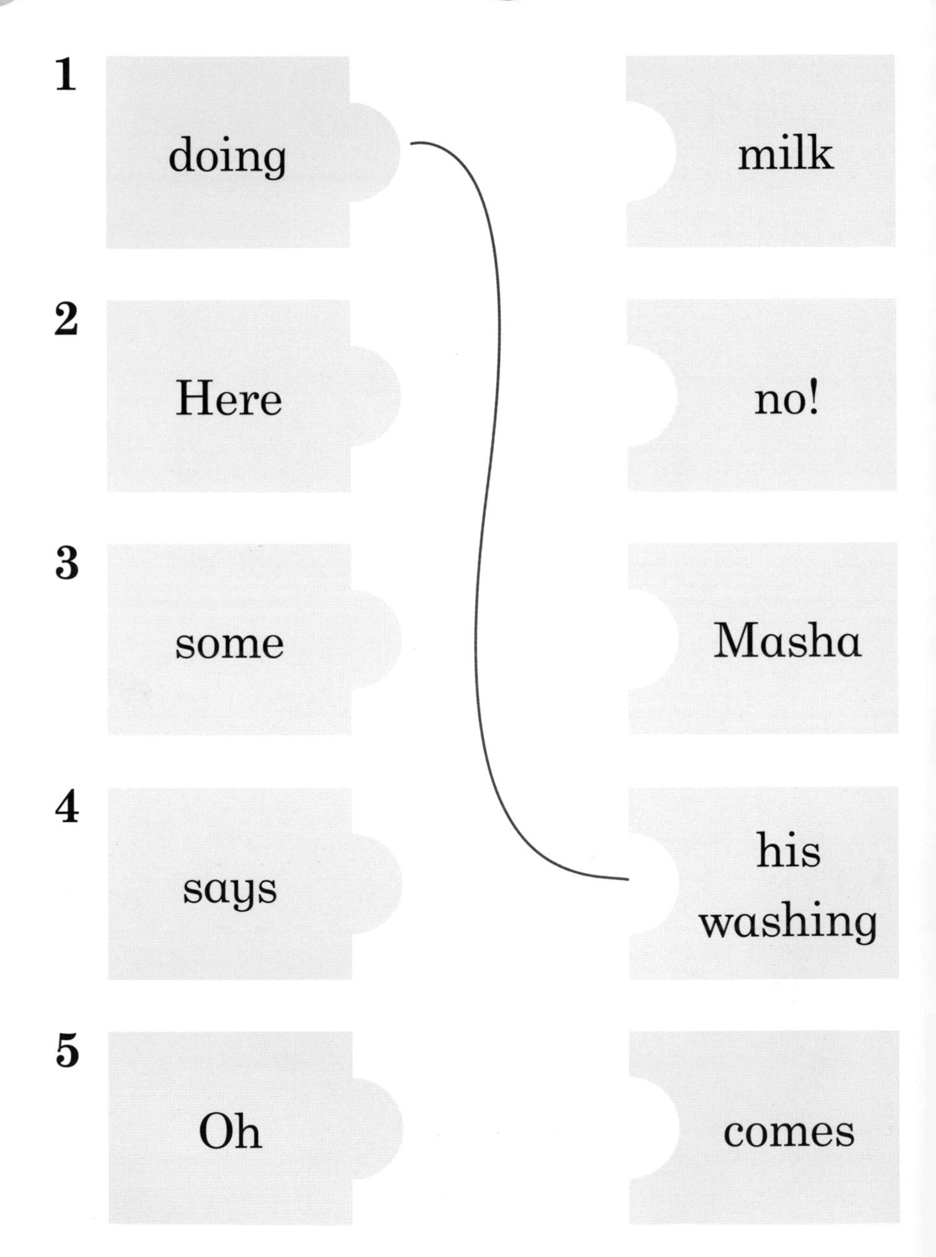

7 **Write *is*, *are*, *has*, or *washes*.**

1 Pig Rosie ....is..........
listening to music.

2 Masha ....
a shower.

3 Bear ....
Masha's clothes.

4 Now, the clothes ....
clean and wet.

5 Masha .... clean
and wet, too!

8 Look and read. Write *yes* or *no*.

1 Masha has a shower. ......yes......

2 Bear washes Masha's hair. ....

3 The clothes are clean and wet. ....

4 Masha is dirty and wet. ....

9 Talk about the two pictures with a friend. How are they different? Use the words in the box.

Masha	clothes	likes	making
looks	wearing	new	Bear

Bear is making new clothes in picture a. Masha is wearing new clothes in picture b.

10 Circle the correct answers. 

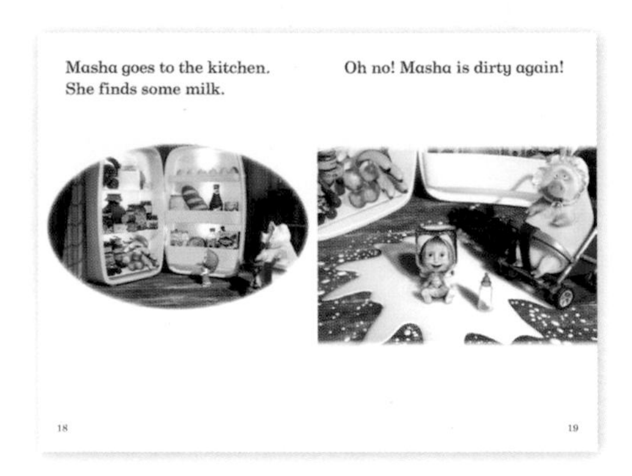

1 Where does Masha go?

a She goes to the garden.

b She goes to the kitchen.

2 Who is with Masha?

a Pig Rosie is with Masha.

b Bear is with Masha.

3 What does Masha find?

a She finds some clothes.

b She finds some milk.

4 Where does the milk go?

a On the table.

b On the floor.

11 Read the questions. Write the answers.

Masha has a shower.

Bear washes Masha's clothes. Then, he makes new clothes.

Masha goes to the kitchen. She finds some food.

"Oh, nice!" says Masha.

20 21

1 Does Masha have a shower?

Yes, she has a shower.

2 Does Pig Rosie wash Masha's clothes?

....

3 Does Bear make new clothes?

....

4 Does Masha go to the bathroom?

....

12 Look at the letters. Write the words.

r e w o s h

1 Masha has a shower.

s h a w s e

2 Bear .... Masha's clothes.

e t h o l c s

3 Bear makes new ....

n e k t h i c

4 Masha goes to the ....

m e s o

5 She finds .... food.

13 Look and read. Put a ✓ or a ✗ in the boxes.

1. This is a shower. ✗
2. Pig Rosie is tired. ☐
3. Masha is dirty. ☐
4. This is Bear. ☐
5. This is jam. ☐

14 Read the text and choose the correct words.

1 Masha is dirty

a too.

b again.

2 Masha . . . a shower.

a has

b does

3 Bear makes . . . clothes.

a old

b new

4 Masha finds . . . jam.

a any

b some

5 Bear is

a tired.

b angry.

15 Read the text. Choose the correct words and write them next to 1—4.

1	can	could	cannot
2	give	gives	giving
3	is	are	is not
4	sad	happy	dirty

Oh no! Bear [1] ....cannot........ make new clothes. Bear [2] .... Masha the baby clothes. Now, Masha [3] .... the baby, and Pig Rosie is the mommy. Pig Rosie is [4] .... Bear is happy, too!

16 Write the correct sentences. 

1 cannot | Bear | make | clothes | new | .

Bear cannot make new clothes.

2 the | Masha | clothes | has | baby | .

3 the | baby | Masha | is | .

4 mommy | is | the | Pig | Rosie | .

17 Look at the picture and read the questions. Write the answers.

1 What is Masha wearing?

Masha is wearing the baby clothes.

2 Who is Pig Rosie?

She is the ....

3 Who is happy?

.... are happy.

18 Do the crossword.  

Across

3 Masha wants to . . . with Pig Rosie.

4 Masha goes to Bear's . . .

5 Bear is doing his . . .

Down

1 Masha wants some milk for her . . .

2 Bear washes Masha's . . .

19 Order the story. Write 1—4.

.... Bear is doing his washing. Here comes Masha. She is dirty! Masha has a shower, and Bear washes her clothes.

.... Bear is tired. He gives Masha the baby clothes. Now, Masha is the baby, and Pig Rosie is the mommy. They are happy!

...1... Masha wants some milk for her baby. Pig Rosie is the baby. They go to Bear's house.

.... Masha goes to the kitchen. She finds some milk. Oh no! Masha is dirty again—and again!

Visit **www.ladybirdeducation.co.uk**
for more FREE Ladybird Readers resources

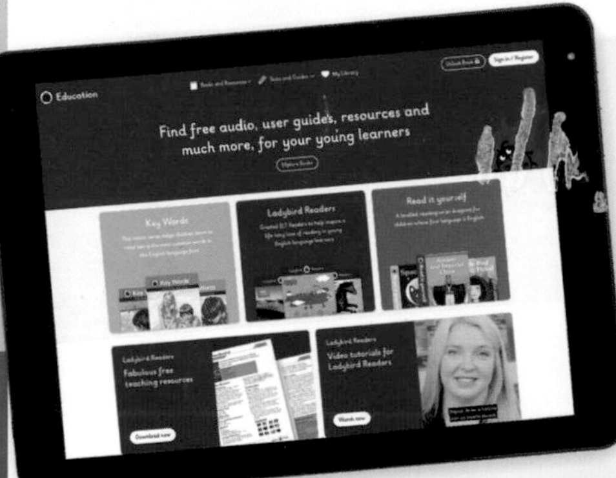

- ✓ Digital edition of every title*
- ✓ Audio tracks (US/UK)
- ✓ Answer keys
- ✓ Lesson plans

- ✓ Role-plays
- ✓ Classroom display material
- ✓ Flashcards
- ✓ User guides

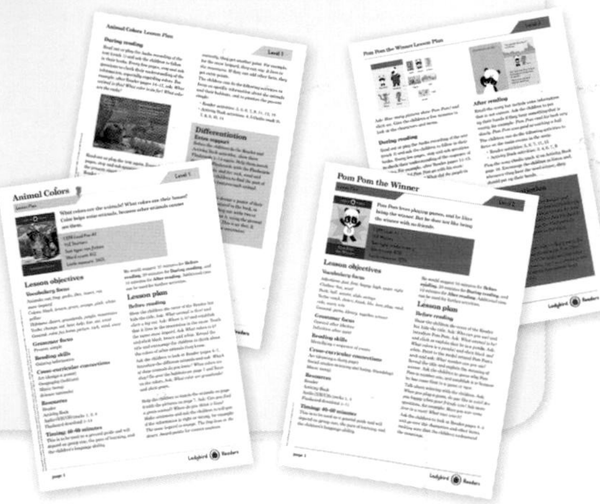

Register and sign up to the newsletter to receive your FREE classroom resource pack!

*Ladybird Readers series only. Not applicable to *Peppa Pig* books.
Digital versions of Ladybird Readers books available once book has been purchased.